We know very little about Aesop's life in Greece in the 6th Century BC. We believe he was born in Thrace and died about 564 BC. He was probably a slave who was later freed by his master, and was said to be deformed but very clever and witty.

In later years he lived at the court of King Croesus, who sent him on a journey to the Temple of Apollo at Delphi. Here he made the Delphians so angry that they pushed him over a steep cliff to his death.

Aesop did not write down his fables. He told many people the stories and they remembered them. It was nearly two hundred years later before all the stories were collected together and published.

The fables were not published in English until the 15th Century, but since then they have been read by people all over the world. Their moral lessons are as true today as they were 2,500 years ago when Aesop was alive.

This carving of Aesop, made in marble, is in the Villa Albani in Rome. It is a copy of a Greek original, probably carved by Lysipus in the 6th Century BC, during Aesop's lifetime.

Aesop's Fables

retold by Marie Stuart

with illustrations by
Robert Ayton

Ladybird Books: Two Continents

Library of Congress Cataloging in Publication Data

Stuart, Marie
   Aesop's Fables

   SUMMARY: Twenty-two of Aesop's famous fables with the moral of each framed in a box.

   [1. Fables] I. Ayton, Robert. II. Aesopus. Fabulae. III. Title.

PZ8.2.S89Ae   813'.5'4 (398.2)   76-52370   ISBN 0-8467-0306-8

Made in England

Contents

The dog and his reflection

One day, a dog took a bone from a shop.
He ran off with it
before anyone could catch him.

He came to a river and went over the bridge.
As he looked down into the water,
he saw another dog with a bone!

He did not know that the dog he saw
in the water was a reflection of himself.

"That dog has a big bone.
It is as big as mine," he said. "I will jump
into the water and take it from him."

So in he jumped.

When he was in the water, he could not see
the other dog, and he could not see
the other bone either.

He had lost his own bone, too, because it fell
as he jumped in.

So, because he was greedy, he got nothing
in the end.

Moral:

*If you want more because you are greedy,
in the end you might find you have less.*

The fox without a tail

One day a fox ran into a trap.
He pulled and pulled to get away from it.
At last he did, but his tail came off.
It was left in the trap.

He did not like the way he looked without a
tail.
"All the other foxes will make fun of me,"
he said.

"What can I do?
I know, I will make them think it is better
not to have a tail."

So he said to the other foxes,
"You would look better without tails.
What use are they anyway? Look at me.
I can run very fast because I have no tail."

But one old fox said,
"You say that, only because you have lost
your own tail. That is why you do not want us
to have tails.
We like our tails, and we shall keep them,
thank you."

Moral : *Wise people are not easily fooled.*

The shepherd boy and the wolf

Once there was a boy who lived on a farm.
Every day he had to take his father's sheep
to a hill a long way off.
He did not like being there on his own.

One day, he said to himself,
"I will call Wolf! Wolf!
Then everyone will think that a wolf has come
to eat my sheep.

People will run to help me. It will be fun
when they find out there is no wolf after all."

So he did call "Wolf! Wolf!"
and everyone ran to help him.

When they came he did not thank them.
He just said, "There is no wolf.
It was only a joke. Now you will all
have to go back home again."

He did this three times.
Each time he told them that there was no wolf.

Then one day the wolf **did** come.
"Help! help! The wolf is here!" called the boy.

But everyone said,
"We know that there is no wolf. He just calls
us for fun. There is no danger.
This time we will not go."

So they did not go and the wolf
killed all the sheep.

Moral:

*If we tell lies, no one will believe us when we
speak the truth.*

The fir tree and the bramble

One day, on a hill top, a fir tree said
to a bramble bush.
"Look at me, I am tall, strong, graceful and
very beautiful.

What good are you ?
You are small, ugly and untidy."

This made the bramble bush
very unhappy because it knew
the fir tree was right.

But next day
some men carrying axes,
came up the hill.

They started to chop down the fir tree.
They wanted to use it to make a new house.

"Oh dear !" cried the fir tree,
as it started to fall.

"I wish I were a bramble bush,
then the men would not have cut me down."

Moral :

People who are too proud may be sorry later.

The boastful traveller

A man once went to a place
he had never been to before. It was a long way
off and he was there for a year. When he went
home, he wanted to talk about it all the time.

Everyone said,
"Why is he always telling us about that place?
We don't want to know about it."

They asked him, "Why did you come back
if it was so nice?"

"I came back to tell you about it,"
  said the man, and he went on talking.

"In that place," he said,
"all the men can jump well.

One day we wanted to see who could jump
the best. So we all had a try.
My jump was the best.
I am a very good jumper.
If you had been there at the time, you would
have seen how good I am."

"We do not have to go all that way to see
  you jump," said one of the men.
"You can let us see how well you can do it here.
So jump **now**!"

Moral :

People who boast are soon found out.

The ant and the dove

One hot day, an ant went to the river
to get a drink of water.
But he fell in and could not get out.

A dove saw that the ant was in danger.
"I must help him," she said.
"If I pick up this leaf and drop it in the water,
the ant can get on it.
It will be like a little boat."

So the dove dropped a leaf in the water
and the ant climbed onto it.

"Thank you, Mrs. Dove," called the ant.
"I will help you one day."

Soon after, a man came along with a bow
and arrow. He saw the dove on the tree
and was going to shoot at her.

Just then the ant came along and bit the man
on the leg.

This made the man jump and his arrow
went up into the sky.

The arrow missed the dove, so she flew away out of danger.

"Thank you little ant," cooed the dove. "You did help me after all."

Moral : *No-one is too little to be helpful.*

The crow and the fox

One day a big, black crow, found some cheese.

"I will fly up into this tree with it," she said.
"I want to eat it now."

A fox came by and saw the bird.
He saw the cheese as well.
He, too, wanted to eat the cheese.

He went round and round the tree
while he thought how he could get the cheese.

Then he said to the crow,
"You look very nice.
If you can sing very nicely as well,
I think you must be Queen of all the birds."

The crow was very pleased.
She liked to be called a Queen.
"Yes, I can sing," she said.

But as she said this
the cheese fell from her beak.

Down to the ground it fell.
The fox picked up the cheese and ran away.

"You may be Queen of the birds.
You may look nice and you may sing well.
But you do not think very well,"
he said, as he ran off.

Moral :

Beware of people who say nice things they do not mean.

The boys and the frogs

One day, four boys went out to play
near a pond.

Some frogs lived in the pond. It was their home.

One bad boy saw the frogs and said
to the other boys,
"Come on ! Let's make them jump
out of the water. It will be fun !"

So they all looked for something to throw
at the frogs.

A little frog saw what they were doing.

He did not like what he saw.

So he hopped onto a floating leaf
in front of the boys.

"STOP !"
shouted the little frog.

"You would not like to have stones
thrown at you if you were frogs.
It may be fun for you, but it is no fun for us !"

Moral :

*Do not do things to other people that you would
not like done to you.*

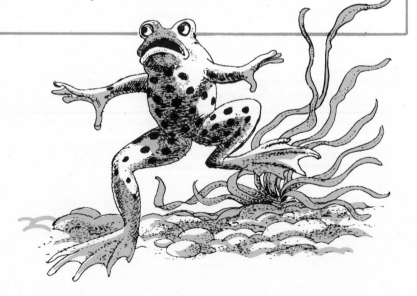

Who will bell the cat

Once some mice lived in a house.

A big cat lived in the house too.

Every day she liked to eat some of the mice.

At last they said to one another,
"This must stop, or soon we shall all be eaten.
Let us all think what we can do."

After a time an old mouse said,
"I know what we can do.
One of us must put a bell on the cat.

The bell will tell us when she is near
and when we must stay at home.
After she has gone away, we can come
out again."

"Yes. That will be a wise thing to do.
Let us do that," they all said.

"But which one of us will put the bell on her?"
said the old mouse.

"I am too old, I cannot run very fast
so I don't think I can do it."

"So are we," said some of the others.

"And we are too little," said the baby mice.

In the end no-one would do it.

So the bell was never put on the cat
and she went on eating the mice.

Moral:
Some things are more easily said than done.

The raven and the jug

A big, black raven wanted a drink.

She saw a big jug with water at the bottom.

She could not reach the water
and wondered what to do.

"I know" she said.
"I shall put some stones in the jug.
Then the water will come up to the top."

After the first stone, the water rose a little.
Then she put in another stone,
and the water rose more.

She put more and more stones in
until the water came up to the top of the jug.

"Now I can reach the water.
At last I can have a drink," said the raven.

So she had a very long drink.

Moral:
If you try hard enough, you may find you can do something that at first seems very difficult.

The dog in the manger

One day a dog ran into a stable and jumped into the manger.

The manger had some hay in it.

When the horse and cow wanted to eat their hay, the dog would not let them.

"You don't eat hay, so you don't need it," said the cow.

"We want the hay. It is ours. It is our dinner,"
said the horse.

But the dog said, "If I can't eat it,
then I shall not let you eat it either!"

"Why ?" asked the cow.

"Why ?" asked the horse.

"Because I don't like to see you eat
 what I can't eat too," said the dog,
"Go away !"

So the horse and the cow
had to go away hungry.

Moral :
Do not stop others having what you don't need.

The lion and the hare

Once a lion found a hare.
He was just going to eat her
when a stag ran by.

"That stag will make me a bigger dinner,"
he said.

So he let the hare go and ran after the stag.
But the stag could run very, very fast
and soon it got right away.

When the lion saw
that he could not catch the stag, he said,
"I will go back for the hare."

But when he came to the place where the hare
had been, he found that she had gone.

"I should have had her for my dinner
when I first saw her," said the lion.

"I wanted too much and now I have nothing."

Moral :

*It is sometimes wiser to be content with what
you have.*

The fox and the grapes

A fox saw some nice grapes.

"They look good," he said.

"I want to eat them,
but they are too high for me.
I must try jumping for them."
He jumped and jumped.

Again and again he jumped but he could not
reach the grapes.

So he said, "I can see now that they are green.
They are not sweet. I do not like green grapes.
They are sour. I don't want them."

So he went away without any.

He knew that the grapes were really very nice.
He just said they were sour
because he could not reach them.

Moral :

*It is silly to say that you do not want something
just because you cannot have it.*

The crow and the swan

A crow once saw a swan and said to her,
"How nice you look ! I wish I were white like you.
I do not like being black."

He saw that the swan was always in the water.

"If I get in the water,
I may become white too," he said.

So he got into the water,
but he was still black when he came out.

"Let me think," he said.
"If I **stay** in the water
that may make me white."

Before the crow went into the water, he could fly about to look for food.
He always found something to eat.

He did not like fish and could find nothing else to eat in the water.

So he did not live very long,
nor did he become white.

Moral :

Think well before you copy other people.

Brother and sister

Once there was a man who had two children, a boy and a girl. The boy was good looking, but the girl was not.

One day they found a mirror and for the first time, saw what they looked like. The boy was very pleased.

He said to his sister, "How handsome I am! I look much nicer than you!"

The girl did not like what he said
and gave her brother a push.
"Go away!" she said.

Their father saw what was happening and
said to the boy, "You must always
be good as well as **look** good."

And to the girl he said,

"My dear, if you help everyone and do your best
to please, everyone will love you.
It will not matter that you are
not as good looking as your brother."

Moral :
*It is better to **be** good than to be just good looking.*

The fox and the lion

One day a fox saw a lion.

It was the first time he had ever seen one.

The lion looked so big
that the fox did not know what to do.
He ran away as fast as he possibly could.

Soon he saw the lion again.

This time the fox said,
"I saw you the other day.
I don't like the look of you. You are too big.
You might want to eat me."

And he ran away again.

As he ran, he said to himself,
"The lion did not eat me last time."

So this time he did not run so fast.

Next day he saw the lion again and did not
run away at all.

"Good morning, Mr. Lion," he said.

"I have seen you before. You do not look so big today. I am not afraid of you any more."

So he sat down to have a long chat with the lion.

Moral:

Things are not always what they seem to be at first.

The goose that laid the golden eggs

Once an old man and an old woman
had a goose.
Their goose was not like other geese
because its eggs were different.
They were made of gold.

Every day the goose laid a golden egg
for the old man and the old woman.

They sold the eggs for a lot of money.
But the more money they had
the more they wanted.

They said, "If our goose lays golden eggs
she must be made of gold.
So let us cut her open
and get out all the gold at once.
Then we will have more money."

So they killed the goose, but found no gold.

When their goose was cut open they saw
that she was just like any other goose.

And after that there were no more golden eggs.
So they did not get any more money.
They had nothing left in the end.

Moral : *A greedy man can lose all he has.*

The bear and the travellers

One day, two men were on a journey
when they saw a bear.

At first, the bear did not see them.

One man got up into a tree
as fast as he could.

The other man was slow.
"Please help me up," he called.

But the first man went further up the tree
and left him on his own.

"What can I do?"
said the man under the tree.

"If I run away, the bear will see me.
If he sees me, he will eat me."

So he lay on the ground and did not move.

The bear came up and walked all around him.

At last it went away.

The man in the tree came down.

He said, "The bear came very close to you.
Did he say anything?"

"Yes," said the other man.

The bear said, "Never go for a walk with a man
who leaves you when you are in danger."

Moral :

*A real friend will not leave you to face trouble
alone.*

The wind and the sun

One day the wind said to the sun,
"Look at that man walking along the road.
I can get his cloak off
more quickly than you can."

"We will see about that," said the sun.
"I will let you try first."

So the wind tried to make the man
take off his cloak. He blew and blew,
but the man only pulled his cloak
more closely around himself.

"I give up," said the wind at last.
"I cannot get his cloak off."

Then the sun tried.
He shone as hard as he could.
The man soon became hot
and took off his cloak.

"I have won," said the sun.
"I made him take his cloak off."

Moral:
Kindness often gets things done more quickly than force.

The fox and the stork

One day, a fox said to a stork,
"Would you like to come to my house
for dinner?"

"Yes, please," said the stork.
"That will be very nice."

But when the stork reached the fox's house,
he found that the fox had put the dinner
on two flat plates.

The stork could not eat anything
because of his long beak.

The fox soon ate his own dinner
and then said to the stork,
"Don't you like your dinner?
If you cannot eat any of it
then I will eat it for you."

So he had his own dinner
and the stork's dinner as well.

Soon after, the stork asked the fox to dinner.

The stork put the food in two jugs
which had long necks.

This time it was the fox
who could not reach the food.

He had to watch
while the stork ate both dinners.

Moral:

*If you play mean tricks on other people,
they might do the same to you.*

The trees and the axe

Once a man wanted to cut down some trees
to make a house, but he could not use his axe
because it had no handle.

So he went to the top of a hill
where there were many trees and said to them,
"May I take a tree from this hill?"

But he did not tell them why.

The trees said to one another,
"Let us give him a very little tree.
Then he will go away
and not ask us for anything more."

So they gave him a little tree and the man
went home.

When he got there
he made a handle for his axe.

Then he went back to the hill
and began to cut down the other trees.

"If we had not let him have the little tree he could not have cut us down," they said.

But it was too late.

The trees were all cut down.

Moral:
Be careful when you give way over small things, or you may have to give way over big ones.

The man and the partridge

One day, a fat partridge who was very hungry, wandered into a bird trap.

She gobbled up the food that was in the trap and then found that she could not get out.

The man who had set the trap arrived soon after.

He was very pleased to see such a plump bird in his trap.

The partridge was very unhappy
and begged him to let her go.

"Oh please, good sir," she pleaded,
"If you will set me free,
I will lead all my friends into your trap.
Then you will have many more birds to eat."

The man took the plump partridge
from his trap and said, "If you would do that,
then you surely deserve to die.
You are a wicked bird to want to do
such a shameful thing."

Having said this,
he took the partridge home for his supper.

Moral : *No-one loves a traitor.*